BEST EVER

WHEREAS IT HAS BEEN DETERMINED THAT YOUR EFFORTS AND ACCOMPLISHMENTS HAVE NOT GONE UNNOTICED, THIS CERTIFICATE OF APPRECIATION HEREBY PROCLAIMS THAT:

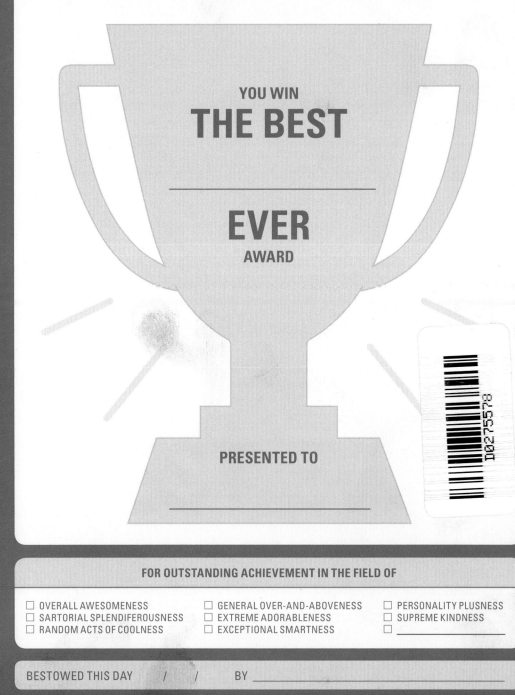

YOU WIN

THE BEST

EVER

AWARD

PRESENTED TO

FOR OUTSTANDING ACHIEVEMENT IN THE FIELD OF

- ☐ OVERALL AWESOMENESS
- ☐ SARTORIAL SPLENDIFEROUSNESS
- ☐ RANDOM ACTS OF COOLNESS
- ☐ GENERAL OVER-AND-ABOVENESS
- ☐ EXTREME ADORABLENESS
- ☐ EXCEPTIONAL SMARTNESS
- ☐ PERSONALITY PLUSNESS
- ☐ SUPREME KINDNESS
- ☐ _____

BESTOWED THIS DAY ___ / ___ / ___ BY _____

"WINNER, WINNER, CHICKEN DINNER"

BEST EVER

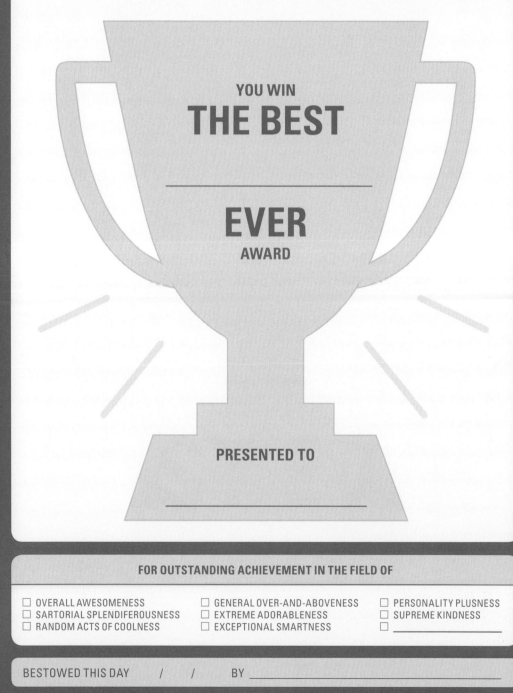

WHEREAS IT HAS BEEN DETERMINED THAT YOUR EFFORTS AND ACCOMPLISHMENTS HAVE NOT GONE UNNOTICED, THIS CERTIFICATE OF APPRECIATION HEREBY PROCLAIMS THAT:

YOU WIN

THE BEST

_____

EVER

AWARD

PRESENTED TO

_____

FOR OUTSTANDING ACHIEVEMENT IN THE FIELD OF

☐ OVERALL AWESOMENESS
☐ SARTORIAL SPLENDIFEROUSNESS
☐ RANDOM ACTS OF COOLNESS

☐ GENERAL OVER-AND-ABOVENESS
☐ EXTREME ADORABLENESS
☐ EXCEPTIONAL SMARTNESS

☐ PERSONALITY PLUSNESS
☐ SUPREME KINDNESS
☐ _____

BESTOWED THIS DAY   /   /   BY _____

"WINNER, WINNER, CHICKEN DINNER"

BEST EVER

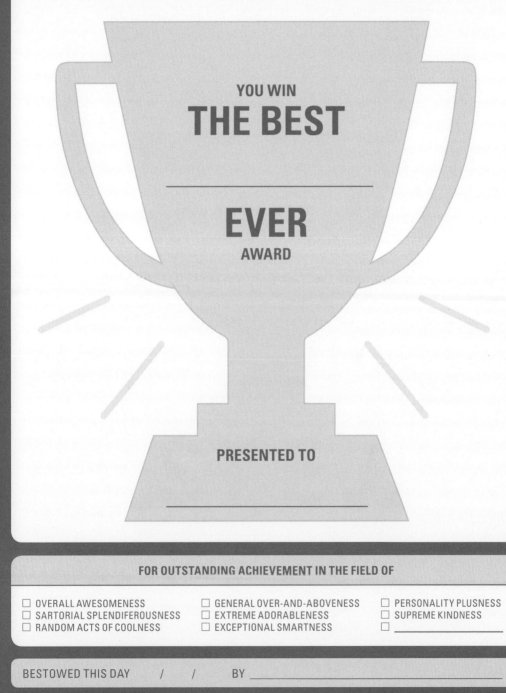

WHEREAS IT HAS BEEN DETERMINED THAT YOUR EFFORTS AND ACCOMPLISHMENTS HAVE NOT GONE UNNOTICED, THIS CERTIFICATE OF APPRECIATION HEREBY PROCLAIMS THAT:

YOU WIN

THE BEST

_____

EVER

AWARD

PRESENTED TO

_____

FOR OUTSTANDING ACHIEVEMENT IN THE FIELD OF

☐ OVERALL AWESOMENESS
☐ SARTORIAL SPLENDIFEROUSNESS
☐ RANDOM ACTS OF COOLNESS

☐ GENERAL OVER-AND-ABOVENESS
☐ EXTREME ADORABLENESS
☐ EXCEPTIONAL SMARTNESS

☐ PERSONALITY PLUSNESS
☐ SUPREME KINDNESS
☐ _____

BESTOWED THIS DAY ____ / ____ / ____ BY _____

"WINNER, WINNER, CHICKEN DINNER"

BEST EVER

WHEREAS IT HAS BEEN DETERMINED THAT YOUR EFFORTS AND ACCOMPLISHMENTS
HAVE NOT GONE UNNOTICED, THIS CERTIFICATE OF APPRECIATION HEREBY PROCLAIMS THAT:

YOU WIN

THE BEST

_____

EVER

AWARD

PRESENTED TO

_____

FOR OUTSTANDING ACHIEVEMENT IN THE FIELD OF

☐ OVERALL AWESOMENESS   ☐ GENERAL OVER-AND-ABOVENESS   ☐ PERSONALITY PLUSNESS
☐ SARTORIAL SPLENDIFEROUSNESS   ☐ EXTREME ADORABLENESS   ☐ SUPREME KINDNESS
☐ RANDOM ACTS OF COOLNESS   ☐ EXCEPTIONAL SMARTNESS   ☐ _____

BESTOWED THIS DAY   /   /   BY _____

"WINNER, WINNER, CHICKEN DINNER"

BEST EVER

YOU WIN

THE BEST

_____

EVER

AWARD

PRESENTED TO

_____

FOR OUTSTANDING ACHIEVEMENT IN THE FIELD OF

- ☐ OVERALL AWESOMENESS
- ☐ SARTORIAL SPLENDIFEROUSNESS
- ☐ RANDOM ACTS OF COOLNESS
- ☐ GENERAL OVER-AND-ABOVENESS
- ☐ EXTREME ADORABLENESS
- ☐ EXCEPTIONAL SMARTNESS
- ☐ PERSONALITY PLUSNESS
- ☐ SUPREME KINDNESS
- ☐ _____

BESTOWED THIS DAY   /   /   BY _____

"WINNER, WINNER, CHICKEN DINNER"

BEST EVER

WHEREAS IT HAS BEEN DETERMINED THAT YOUR EFFORTS AND ACCOMPLISHMENTS HAVE NOT GONE UNNOTICED, THIS CERTIFICATE OF APPRECIATION HEREBY PROCLAIMS THAT:

YOU WIN

THE BEST

_____

EVER

AWARD

PRESENTED TO

_____

FOR OUTSTANDING ACHIEVEMENT IN THE FIELD OF

☐ OVERALL AWESOMENESS
☐ SARTORIAL SPLENDIFEROUSNESS
☐ RANDOM ACTS OF COOLNESS

☐ GENERAL OVER-AND-ABOVENESS
☐ EXTREME ADORABLENESS
☐ EXCEPTIONAL SMARTNESS

☐ PERSONALITY PLUSNESS
☐ SUPREME KINDNESS
☐ _____

BESTOWED THIS DAY _____ / _____ / _____ BY _____

"WINNER, WINNER, CHICKEN DINNER"

BEST EVER

WHEREAS IT HAS BEEN DETERMINED THAT YOUR EFFORTS AND ACCOMPLISHMENTS HAVE NOT GONE UNNOTICED, THIS CERTIFICATE OF APPRECIATION HEREBY PROCLAIMS THAT:

YOU WIN

THE BEST

_____

EVER

AWARD

PRESENTED TO

_____

FOR OUTSTANDING ACHIEVEMENT IN THE FIELD OF

☐ OVERALL AWESOMENESS
☐ SARTORIAL SPLENDIFEROUSNESS
☐ RANDOM ACTS OF COOLNESS
☐ GENERAL OVER-AND-ABOVENESS
☐ EXTREME ADORABLENESS
☐ EXCEPTIONAL SMARTNESS
☐ PERSONALITY PLUSNESS
☐ SUPREME KINDNESS
☐ _____

BESTOWED THIS DAY   /   /   BY _____

"WINNER, WINNER, CHICKEN DINNER"

BEST EVER

WHEREAS IT HAS BEEN DETERMINED THAT YOUR EFFORTS AND ACCOMPLISHMENTS
HAVE NOT GONE UNNOTICED, THIS CERTIFICATE OF APPRECIATION HEREBY PROCLAIMS THAT:

YOU WIN
THE BEST

_____

EVER

AWARD

PRESENTED TO

_____

FOR OUTSTANDING ACHIEVEMENT IN THE FIELD OF

☐ OVERALL AWESOMENESS   ☐ GENERAL OVER-AND-ABOVENESS   ☐ PERSONALITY PLUSNESS
☐ SARTORIAL SPLENDIFEROUSNESS   ☐ EXTREME ADORABLENESS   ☐ SUPREME KINDNESS
☐ RANDOM ACTS OF COOLNESS   ☐ EXCEPTIONAL SMARTNESS   ☐ _____

BESTOWED THIS DAY   /   /   BY _____

"WINNER, WINNER, CHICKEN DINNER"

BEST EVER

WHEREAS IT HAS BEEN DETERMINED THAT YOUR EFFORTS AND ACCOMPLISHMENTS HAVE NOT GONE UNNOTICED, THIS CERTIFICATE OF APPRECIATION HEREBY PROCLAIMS THAT:

YOU WIN

THE BEST

_____

EVER

AWARD

PRESENTED TO

_____

FOR OUTSTANDING ACHIEVEMENT IN THE FIELD OF

- ☐ OVERALL AWESOMENESS
- ☐ SARTORIAL SPLENDIFEROUSNESS
- ☐ RANDOM ACTS OF COOLNESS
- ☐ GENERAL OVER-AND-ABOVENESS
- ☐ EXTREME ADORABLENESS
- ☐ EXCEPTIONAL SMARTNESS
- ☐ PERSONALITY PLUSNESS
- ☐ SUPREME KINDNESS
- ☐ _____

BESTOWED THIS DAY   /   /   BY _____

"WINNER, WINNER, CHICKEN DINNER"

BEST EVER

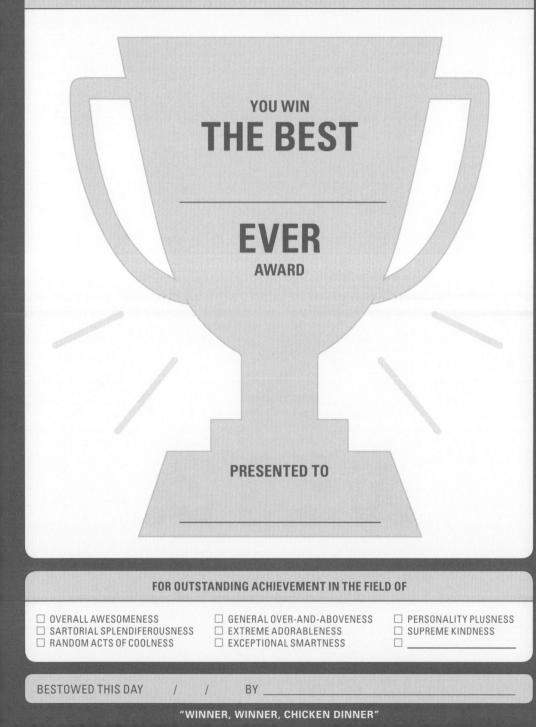

YOU WIN
THE BEST

_____

EVER
AWARD

PRESENTED TO

_____

FOR OUTSTANDING ACHIEVEMENT IN THE FIELD OF

- ☐ OVERALL AWESOMENESS
- ☐ SARTORIAL SPLENDIFEROUSNESS
- ☐ RANDOM ACTS OF COOLNESS
- ☐ GENERAL OVER-AND-ABOVENESS
- ☐ EXTREME ADORABLENESS
- ☐ EXCEPTIONAL SMARTNESS
- ☐ PERSONALITY PLUSNESS
- ☐ SUPREME KINDNESS
- ☐ _____

BESTOWED THIS DAY   /   /   BY _____

"WINNER, WINNER, CHICKEN DINNER"

BEST EVER

WHEREAS IT HAS BEEN DETERMINED THAT YOUR EFFORTS AND ACCOMPLISHMENTS HAVE NOT GONE UNNOTICED, THIS CERTIFICATE OF APPRECIATION HEREBY PROCLAIMS THAT:

YOU WIN
THE BEST

_____

EVER
AWARD

PRESENTED TO

_____

FOR OUTSTANDING ACHIEVEMENT IN THE FIELD OF

- ☐ OVERALL AWESOMENESS
- ☐ SARTORIAL SPLENDIFEROUSNESS
- ☐ RANDOM ACTS OF COOLNESS
- ☐ GENERAL OVER-AND-ABOVENESS
- ☐ EXTREME ADORABLENESS
- ☐ EXCEPTIONAL SMARTNESS
- ☐ PERSONALITY PLUSNESS
- ☐ SUPREME KINDNESS
- ☐ _____

BESTOWED THIS DAY _____ / _____ / _____ BY _____

"WINNER, WINNER, CHICKEN DINNER"

BEST EVER

YOU WIN
THE BEST

_____

EVER

AWARD

PRESENTED TO

_____

FOR OUTSTANDING ACHIEVEMENT IN THE FIELD OF

- ☐ OVERALL AWESOMENESS
- ☐ SARTORIAL SPLENDIFEROUSNESS
- ☐ RANDOM ACTS OF COOLNESS
- ☐ GENERAL OVER-AND-ABOVENESS
- ☐ EXTREME ADORABLENESS
- ☐ EXCEPTIONAL SMARTNESS
- ☐ PERSONALITY PLUSNESS
- ☐ SUPREME KINDNESS
- ☐ _____

BESTOWED THIS DAY   /   /   BY _____

"WINNER, WINNER, CHICKEN DINNER"

BEST EVER

YOU WIN
THE BEST

_____

EVER
AWARD

PRESENTED TO

_____

FOR OUTSTANDING ACHIEVEMENT IN THE FIELD OF

- ☐ OVERALL AWESOMENESS
- ☐ SARTORIAL SPLENDIFEROUSNESS
- ☐ RANDOM ACTS OF COOLNESS
- ☐ GENERAL OVER-AND-ABOVENESS
- ☐ EXTREME ADORABLENESS
- ☐ EXCEPTIONAL SMARTNESS
- ☐ PERSONALITY PLUSNESS
- ☐ SUPREME KINDNESS
- ☐ _____

BESTOWED THIS DAY   /   /   BY _____

"WINNER, WINNER, CHICKEN DINNER"

BEST EVER

WHEREAS IT HAS BEEN DETERMINED THAT YOUR EFFORTS AND ACCOMPLISHMENTS
HAVE NOT GONE UNNOTICED, THIS CERTIFICATE OF APPRECIATION HEREBY PROCLAIMS THAT:

YOU WIN

THE BEST

_____

EVER

AWARD

PRESENTED TO

_____

FOR OUTSTANDING ACHIEVEMENT IN THE FIELD OF

- ☐ OVERALL AWESOMENESS
- ☐ SARTORIAL SPLENDIFEROUSNESS
- ☐ RANDOM ACTS OF COOLNESS
- ☐ GENERAL OVER-AND-ABOVENESS
- ☐ EXTREME ADORABLENESS
- ☐ EXCEPTIONAL SMARTNESS
- ☐ PERSONALITY PLUSNESS
- ☐ SUPREME KINDNESS
- ☐ _____

BESTOWED THIS DAY   /   /   BY _____

"WINNER, WINNER, CHICKEN DINNER"

BEST EVER

WHEREAS IT HAS BEEN DETERMINED THAT YOUR EFFORTS AND ACCOMPLISHMENTS HAVE NOT GONE UNNOTICED, THIS CERTIFICATE OF APPRECIATION HEREBY PROCLAIMS THAT:

YOU WIN

THE BEST

_____

EVER

AWARD

PRESENTED TO

_____

FOR OUTSTANDING ACHIEVEMENT IN THE FIELD OF

☐ OVERALL AWESOMENESS
☐ SARTORIAL SPLENDIFEROUSNESS
☐ RANDOM ACTS OF COOLNESS

☐ GENERAL OVER-AND-ABOVENESS
☐ EXTREME ADORABLENESS
☐ EXCEPTIONAL SMARTNESS

☐ PERSONALITY PLUSNESS
☐ SUPREME KINDNESS
☐ _____

BESTOWED THIS DAY ___ / ___ / ___ BY _____

"WINNER, WINNER, CHICKEN DINNER"

BEST EVER

WHEREAS IT HAS BEEN DETERMINED THAT YOUR EFFORTS AND ACCOMPLISHMENTS HAVE NOT GONE UNNOTICED, THIS CERTIFICATE OF APPRECIATION HEREBY PROCLAIMS THAT:

YOU WIN

THE BEST

_____

EVER

AWARD

PRESENTED TO

_____

FOR OUTSTANDING ACHIEVEMENT IN THE FIELD OF

- ☐ OVERALL AWESOMENESS
- ☐ SARTORIAL SPLENDIFEROUSNESS
- ☐ RANDOM ACTS OF COOLNESS
- ☐ GENERAL OVER-AND-ABOVENESS
- ☐ EXTREME ADORABLENESS
- ☐ EXCEPTIONAL SMARTNESS
- ☐ PERSONALITY PLUSNESS
- ☐ SUPREME KINDNESS
- ☐ _____

BESTOWED THIS DAY ___ / ___ / ___ BY _____

"WINNER, WINNER, CHICKEN DINNER"

BEST EVER

YOU WIN

THE BEST

_____

EVER

AWARD

PRESENTED TO

_____

FOR OUTSTANDING ACHIEVEMENT IN THE FIELD OF

- ☐ OVERALL AWESOMENESS
- ☐ SARTORIAL SPLENDIFEROUSNESS
- ☐ RANDOM ACTS OF COOLNESS
- ☐ GENERAL OVER-AND-ABOVENESS
- ☐ EXTREME ADORABLENESS
- ☐ EXCEPTIONAL SMARTNESS
- ☐ PERSONALITY PLUSNESS
- ☐ SUPREME KINDNESS
- ☐ _____

BESTOWED THIS DAY   /   /   BY _____

"WINNER, WINNER, CHICKEN DINNER"

BEST EVER

WHEREAS IT HAS BEEN DETERMINED THAT YOUR EFFORTS AND ACCOMPLISHMENTS HAVE NOT GONE UNNOTICED, THIS CERTIFICATE OF APPRECIATION HEREBY PROCLAIMS THAT:

YOU WIN

THE BEST

_____

EVER

AWARD

PRESENTED TO

_____

FOR OUTSTANDING ACHIEVEMENT IN THE FIELD OF

- ☐ OVERALL AWESOMENESS
- ☐ SARTORIAL SPLENDIFEROUSNESS
- ☐ RANDOM ACTS OF COOLNESS
- ☐ GENERAL OVER-AND-ABOVENESS
- ☐ EXTREME ADORABLENESS
- ☐ EXCEPTIONAL SMARTNESS
- ☐ PERSONALITY PLUSNESS
- ☐ SUPREME KINDNESS
- ☐ _____

BESTOWED THIS DAY   /   /   BY _____

"WINNER, WINNER, CHICKEN DINNER"

BEST EVER

WHEREAS IT HAS BEEN DETERMINED THAT YOUR EFFORTS AND ACCOMPLISHMENTS HAVE NOT GONE UNNOTICED, THIS CERTIFICATE OF APPRECIATION HEREBY PROCLAIMS THAT:

YOU WIN
THE BEST

_____

EVER

AWARD

PRESENTED TO

_____

FOR OUTSTANDING ACHIEVEMENT IN THE FIELD OF

☐ OVERALL AWESOMENESS
☐ SARTORIAL SPLENDIFEROUSNESS
☐ RANDOM ACTS OF COOLNESS

☐ GENERAL OVER-AND-ABOVENESS
☐ EXTREME ADORABLENESS
☐ EXCEPTIONAL SMARTNESS

☐ PERSONALITY PLUSNESS
☐ SUPREME KINDNESS
☐ _____

BESTOWED THIS DAY ___ / ___ / ___ BY _____

"WINNER, WINNER, CHICKEN DINNER"

BEST EVER

WHEREAS IT HAS BEEN DETERMINED THAT YOUR EFFORTS AND ACCOMPLISHMENTS HAVE NOT GONE UNNOTICED, THIS CERTIFICATE OF APPRECIATION HEREBY PROCLAIMS THAT:

YOU WIN

THE BEST

_____

EVER

AWARD

PRESENTED TO

_____

FOR OUTSTANDING ACHIEVEMENT IN THE FIELD OF

☐ OVERALL AWESOMENESS
☐ SARTORIAL SPLENDIFEROUSNESS
☐ RANDOM ACTS OF COOLNESS

☐ GENERAL OVER-AND-ABOVENESS
☐ EXTREME ADORABLENESS
☐ EXCEPTIONAL SMARTNESS

☐ PERSONALITY PLUSNESS
☐ SUPREME KINDNESS
☐ _____

BESTOWED THIS DAY   /   /   BY _____

"WINNER, WINNER, CHICKEN DINNER"

BEST EVER

WHEREAS IT HAS BEEN DETERMINED THAT YOUR EFFORTS AND ACCOMPLISHMENTS HAVE NOT GONE UNNOTICED, THIS CERTIFICATE OF APPRECIATION HEREBY PROCLAIMS THAT:

YOU WIN

THE BEST

_____

EVER

AWARD

PRESENTED TO

_____

FOR OUTSTANDING ACHIEVEMENT IN THE FIELD OF

- ☐ OVERALL AWESOMENESS
- ☐ SARTORIAL SPLENDIFEROUSNESS
- ☐ RANDOM ACTS OF COOLNESS
- ☐ GENERAL OVER-AND-ABOVENESS
- ☐ EXTREME ADORABLENESS
- ☐ EXCEPTIONAL SMARTNESS
- ☐ PERSONALITY PLUSNESS
- ☐ SUPREME KINDNESS
- ☐ _____

BESTOWED THIS DAY   /   /   BY _____

"WINNER, WINNER, CHICKEN DINNER"

BEST EVER

WHEREAS IT HAS BEEN DETERMINED THAT YOUR EFFORTS AND ACCOMPLISHMENTS HAVE NOT GONE UNNOTICED, THIS CERTIFICATE OF APPRECIATION HEREBY PROCLAIMS THAT:

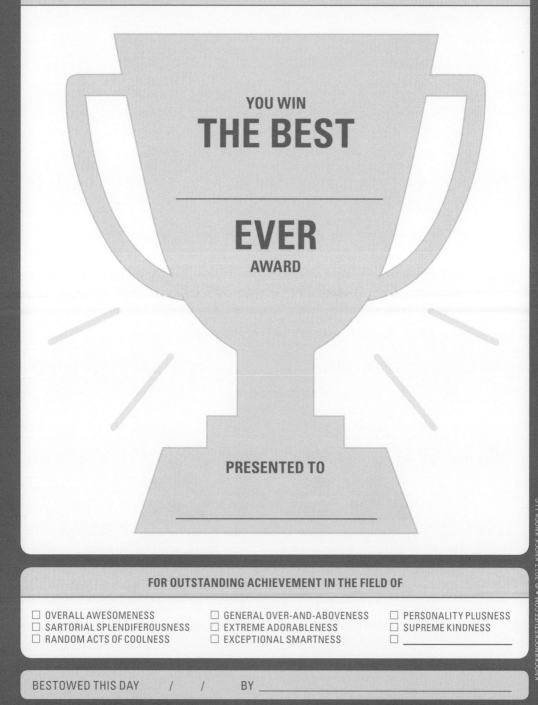

YOU WIN

THE BEST

_____

EVER

AWARD

PRESENTED TO

_____

FOR OUTSTANDING ACHIEVEMENT IN THE FIELD OF

- ☐ OVERALL AWESOMENESS
- ☐ SARTORIAL SPLENDIFEROUSNESS
- ☐ RANDOM ACTS OF COOLNESS

- ☐ GENERAL OVER-AND-ABOVENESS
- ☐ EXTREME ADORABLENESS
- ☐ EXCEPTIONAL SMARTNESS

- ☐ PERSONALITY PLUSNESS
- ☐ SUPREME KINDNESS
- ☐ _____

BESTOWED THIS DAY   /   /   BY _____

"WINNER, WINNER, CHICKEN DINNER"

BEST EVER

WHEREAS IT HAS BEEN DETERMINED THAT YOUR EFFORTS AND ACCOMPLISHMENTS HAVE NOT GONE UNNOTICED, THIS CERTIFICATE OF APPRECIATION HEREBY PROCLAIMS THAT:

YOU WIN

THE BEST

_____

EVER

AWARD

PRESENTED TO

_____

FOR OUTSTANDING ACHIEVEMENT IN THE FIELD OF

☐ OVERALL AWESOMENESS
☐ SARTORIAL SPLENDIFEROUSNESS
☐ RANDOM ACTS OF COOLNESS

☐ GENERAL OVER-AND-ABOVENESS
☐ EXTREME ADORABLENESS
☐ EXCEPTIONAL SMARTNESS

☐ PERSONALITY PLUSNESS
☐ SUPREME KINDNESS
☐ _____

BESTOWED THIS DAY ____ / ____ / ____ BY _____

"WINNER, WINNER, CHICKEN DINNER"

BEST EVER

WHEREAS IT HAS BEEN DETERMINED THAT YOUR EFFORTS AND ACCOMPLISHMENTS HAVE NOT GONE UNNOTICED, THIS CERTIFICATE OF APPRECIATION HEREBY PROCLAIMS THAT:

YOU WIN

THE BEST

_____

EVER

AWARD

PRESENTED TO

_____

FOR OUTSTANDING ACHIEVEMENT IN THE FIELD OF

- ☐ OVERALL AWESOMENESS
- ☐ SARTORIAL SPLENDIFEROUSNESS
- ☐ RANDOM ACTS OF COOLNESS
- ☐ GENERAL OVER-AND-ABOVENESS
- ☐ EXTREME ADORABLENESS
- ☐ EXCEPTIONAL SMARTNESS
- ☐ PERSONALITY PLUSNESS
- ☐ SUPREME KINDNESS
- ☐ _____

BESTOWED THIS DAY ____ / ____ / ____ BY _____

"WINNER, WINNER, CHICKEN DINNER"

BEST EVER

WHEREAS IT HAS BEEN DETERMINED THAT YOUR EFFORTS AND ACCOMPLISHMENTS HAVE NOT GONE UNNOTICED, THIS CERTIFICATE OF APPRECIATION HEREBY PROCLAIMS THAT:

YOU WIN

THE BEST

_____

EVER

AWARD

PRESENTED TO

_____

FOR OUTSTANDING ACHIEVEMENT IN THE FIELD OF

- ☐ OVERALL AWESOMENESS
- ☐ SARTORIAL SPLENDIFEROUSNESS
- ☐ RANDOM ACTS OF COOLNESS
- ☐ GENERAL OVER-AND-ABOVENESS
- ☐ EXTREME ADORABLENESS
- ☐ EXCEPTIONAL SMARTNESS
- ☐ PERSONALITY PLUSNESS
- ☐ SUPREME KINDNESS
- ☐ _____

BESTOWED THIS DAY   /   /   BY _____

"WINNER, WINNER, CHICKEN DINNER"

BEST EVER

WHEREAS IT HAS BEEN DETERMINED THAT YOUR EFFORTS AND ACCOMPLISHMENTS
HAVE NOT GONE UNNOTICED, THIS CERTIFICATE OF APPRECIATION HEREBY PROCLAIMS THAT:

YOU WIN
THE BEST

_____

EVER
AWARD

PRESENTED TO

_____

FOR OUTSTANDING ACHIEVEMENT IN THE FIELD OF

- ☐ OVERALL AWESOMENESS
- ☐ SARTORIAL SPLENDIFEROUSNESS
- ☐ RANDOM ACTS OF COOLNESS
- ☐ GENERAL OVER-AND-ABOVENESS
- ☐ EXTREME ADORABLENESS
- ☐ EXCEPTIONAL SMARTNESS
- ☐ PERSONALITY PLUSNESS
- ☐ SUPREME KINDNESS
- ☐ _____

BESTOWED THIS DAY   /   /   BY _____

"WINNER, WINNER, CHICKEN DINNER"

BEST EVER

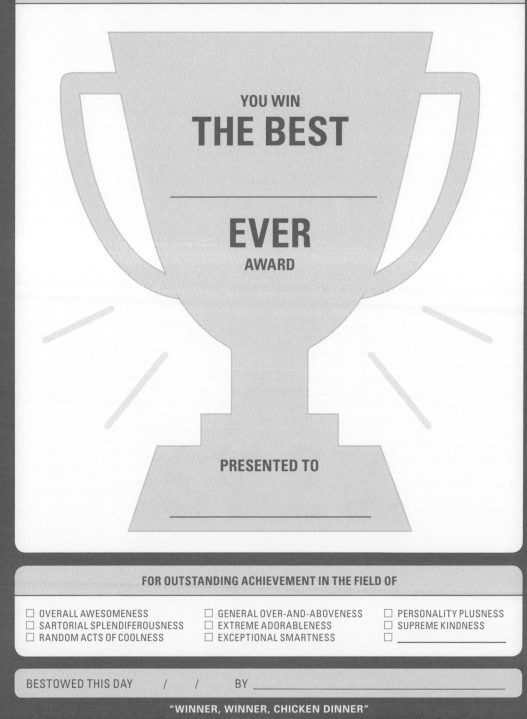

WHEREAS IT HAS BEEN DETERMINED THAT YOUR EFFORTS AND ACCOMPLISHMENTS HAVE NOT GONE UNNOTICED, THIS CERTIFICATE OF APPRECIATION HEREBY PROCLAIMS THAT:

YOU WIN

THE BEST

_____

EVER

AWARD

PRESENTED TO

_____

FOR OUTSTANDING ACHIEVEMENT IN THE FIELD OF

☐ OVERALL AWESOMENESS   ☐ GENERAL OVER-AND-ABOVENESS   ☐ PERSONALITY PLUSNESS
☐ SARTORIAL SPLENDIFEROUSNESS   ☐ EXTREME ADORABLENESS   ☐ SUPREME KINDNESS
☐ RANDOM ACTS OF COOLNESS   ☐ EXCEPTIONAL SMARTNESS   ☐ _____

BESTOWED THIS DAY   /   /   BY _____

"WINNER, WINNER, CHICKEN DINNER"

BEST EVER

WHEREAS IT HAS BEEN DETERMINED THAT YOUR EFFORTS AND ACCOMPLISHMENTS
HAVE NOT GONE UNNOTICED, THIS CERTIFICATE OF APPRECIATION HEREBY PROCLAIMS THAT:

YOU WIN
THE BEST

_____

EVER
AWARD

PRESENTED TO

_____

FOR OUTSTANDING ACHIEVEMENT IN THE FIELD OF

- ☐ OVERALL AWESOMENESS
- ☐ SARTORIAL SPLENDIFEROUSNESS
- ☐ RANDOM ACTS OF COOLNESS
- ☐ GENERAL OVER-AND-ABOVENESS
- ☐ EXTREME ADORABLENESS
- ☐ EXCEPTIONAL SMARTNESS
- ☐ PERSONALITY PLUSNESS
- ☐ SUPREME KINDNESS
- ☐ _____

BESTOWED THIS DAY ____ / ____ / ____ BY _____

"WINNER, WINNER, CHICKEN DINNER"

BEST EVER

YOU WIN

THE BEST

_____

EVER

AWARD

PRESENTED TO

_____

FOR OUTSTANDING ACHIEVEMENT IN THE FIELD OF

- ☐ OVERALL AWESOMENESS
- ☐ SARTORIAL SPLENDIFEROUSNESS
- ☐ RANDOM ACTS OF COOLNESS
- ☐ GENERAL OVER-AND-ABOVENESS
- ☐ EXTREME ADORABLENESS
- ☐ EXCEPTIONAL SMARTNESS
- ☐ PERSONALITY PLUSNESS
- ☐ SUPREME KINDNESS
- ☐ _____

BESTOWED THIS DAY ___ / ___ / ___ BY _____

"WINNER, WINNER, CHICKEN DINNER"

BEST EVER

YOU WIN
THE BEST

_____

EVER

AWARD

PRESENTED TO

_____

FOR OUTSTANDING ACHIEVEMENT IN THE FIELD OF

- ☐ OVERALL AWESOMENESS
- ☐ SARTORIAL SPLENDIFEROUSNESS
- ☐ RANDOM ACTS OF COOLNESS
- ☐ GENERAL OVER-AND-ABOVENESS
- ☐ EXTREME ADORABLENESS
- ☐ EXCEPTIONAL SMARTNESS
- ☐ PERSONALITY PLUSNESS
- ☐ SUPREME KINDNESS
- ☐ _____

BESTOWED THIS DAY ___ / ___ / ___ BY _____

"WINNER, WINNER, CHICKEN DINNER"

BEST EVER

WHEREAS IT HAS BEEN DETERMINED THAT YOUR EFFORTS AND ACCOMPLISHMENTS HAVE NOT GONE UNNOTICED, THIS CERTIFICATE OF APPRECIATION HEREBY PROCLAIMS THAT:

YOU WIN

THE BEST

_____

EVER

AWARD

PRESENTED TO

_____

FOR OUTSTANDING ACHIEVEMENT IN THE FIELD OF

☐ OVERALL AWESOMENESS
☐ SARTORIAL SPLENDIFEROUSNESS
☐ RANDOM ACTS OF COOLNESS

☐ GENERAL OVER-AND-ABOVENESS
☐ EXTREME ADORABLENESS
☐ EXCEPTIONAL SMARTNESS

☐ PERSONALITY PLUSNESS
☐ SUPREME KINDNESS
☐ _____

BESTOWED THIS DAY ____ / ____ / ____ BY _____

"WINNER, WINNER, CHICKEN DINNER"

BEST EVER

WHEREAS IT HAS BEEN DETERMINED THAT YOUR EFFORTS AND ACCOMPLISHMENTS HAVE NOT GONE UNNOTICED, THIS CERTIFICATE OF APPRECIATION HEREBY PROCLAIMS THAT:

YOU WIN

THE BEST

_____

EVER

AWARD

PRESENTED TO

_____

FOR OUTSTANDING ACHIEVEMENT IN THE FIELD OF

☐ OVERALL AWESOMENESS   ☐ GENERAL OVER-AND-ABOVENESS   ☐ PERSONALITY PLUSNESS
☐ SARTORIAL SPLENDIFEROUSNESS   ☐ EXTREME ADORABLENESS   ☐ SUPREME KINDNESS
☐ RANDOM ACTS OF COOLNESS   ☐ EXCEPTIONAL SMARTNESS   ☐ _____

BESTOWED THIS DAY   /   /   BY _____

"WINNER, WINNER, CHICKEN DINNER"

BEST EVER

WHEREAS IT HAS BEEN DETERMINED THAT YOUR EFFORTS AND ACCOMPLISHMENTS HAVE NOT GONE UNNOTICED, THIS CERTIFICATE OF APPRECIATION HEREBY PROCLAIMS THAT:

YOU WIN

THE BEST

EVER

AWARD

PRESENTED TO

FOR OUTSTANDING ACHIEVEMENT IN THE FIELD OF

- ☐ OVERALL AWESOMENESS
- ☐ SARTORIAL SPLENDIFEROUSNESS
- ☐ RANDOM ACTS OF COOLNESS
- ☐ GENERAL OVER-AND-ABOVENESS
- ☐ EXTREME ADORABLENESS
- ☐ EXCEPTIONAL SMARTNESS
- ☐ PERSONALITY PLUSNESS
- ☐ SUPREME KINDNESS
- ☐ _____

BESTOWED THIS DAY _____ / _____ / _____ BY _____

"WINNER, WINNER, CHICKEN DINNER"

BEST EVER

WHEREAS IT HAS BEEN DETERMINED THAT YOUR EFFORTS AND ACCOMPLISHMENTS HAVE NOT GONE UNNOTICED, THIS CERTIFICATE OF APPRECIATION HEREBY PROCLAIMS THAT:

YOU WIN

THE BEST

_____

EVER

AWARD

PRESENTED TO

_____

FOR OUTSTANDING ACHIEVEMENT IN THE FIELD OF

- ☐ OVERALL AWESOMENESS
- ☐ SARTORIAL SPLENDIFEROUSNESS
- ☐ RANDOM ACTS OF COOLNESS
- ☐ GENERAL OVER-AND-ABOVENESS
- ☐ EXTREME ADORABLENESS
- ☐ EXCEPTIONAL SMARTNESS
- ☐ PERSONALITY PLUSNESS
- ☐ SUPREME KINDNESS
- ☐ _____

BESTOWED THIS DAY _____ / _____ / _____ BY _____

"WINNER, WINNER, CHICKEN DINNER"

BEST EVER

WHEREAS IT HAS BEEN DETERMINED THAT YOUR EFFORTS AND ACCOMPLISHMENTS HAVE NOT GONE UNNOTICED, THIS CERTIFICATE OF APPRECIATION HEREBY PROCLAIMS THAT:

YOU WIN
THE BEST

_____

EVER
AWARD

PRESENTED TO

_____

FOR OUTSTANDING ACHIEVEMENT IN THE FIELD OF

☐ OVERALL AWESOMENESS
☐ SARTORIAL SPLENDIFEROUSNESS
☐ RANDOM ACTS OF COOLNESS

☐ GENERAL OVER-AND-ABOVENESS
☐ EXTREME ADORABLENESS
☐ EXCEPTIONAL SMARTNESS

☐ PERSONALITY PLUSNESS
☐ SUPREME KINDNESS
☐ _____

BESTOWED THIS DAY ___ / ___ / ___ BY _____

"WINNER, WINNER, CHICKEN DINNER"

BEST EVER

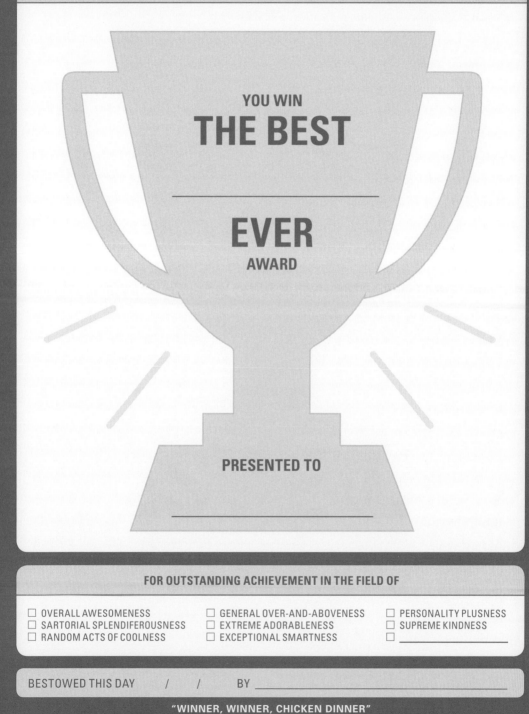

WHEREAS IT HAS BEEN DETERMINED THAT YOUR EFFORTS AND ACCOMPLISHMENTS HAVE NOT GONE UNNOTICED, THIS CERTIFICATE OF APPRECIATION HEREBY PROCLAIMS THAT:

YOU WIN

THE BEST

_____

EVER

AWARD

PRESENTED TO

_____

FOR OUTSTANDING ACHIEVEMENT IN THE FIELD OF

- ☐ OVERALL AWESOMENESS
- ☐ SARTORIAL SPLENDIFEROUSNESS
- ☐ RANDOM ACTS OF COOLNESS

- ☐ GENERAL OVER-AND-ABOVENESS
- ☐ EXTREME ADORABLENESS
- ☐ EXCEPTIONAL SMARTNESS

- ☐ PERSONALITY PLUSNESS
- ☐ SUPREME KINDNESS
- ☐ _____

BESTOWED THIS DAY _____ / _____ / _____ BY _____

"WINNER, WINNER, CHICKEN DINNER"

BEST EVER

WHEREAS IT HAS BEEN DETERMINED THAT YOUR EFFORTS AND ACCOMPLISHMENTS
HAVE NOT GONE UNNOTICED, THIS CERTIFICATE OF APPRECIATION HEREBY PROCLAIMS THAT:

YOU WIN

THE BEST

_____

EVER

AWARD

PRESENTED TO

_____

FOR OUTSTANDING ACHIEVEMENT IN THE FIELD OF

☐ OVERALL AWESOMENESS   ☐ GENERAL OVER-AND-ABOVENESS   ☐ PERSONALITY PLUSNESS
☐ SARTORIAL SPLENDIFEROUSNESS ☐ EXTREME ADORABLENESS   ☐ SUPREME KINDNESS
☐ RANDOM ACTS OF COOLNESS   ☐ EXCEPTIONAL SMARTNESS   ☐ _____

BESTOWED THIS DAY   /   /   BY _____

"WINNER, WINNER, CHICKEN DINNER"

BEST EVER

YOU WIN
THE BEST

_____

EVER
AWARD

PRESENTED TO

_____

FOR OUTSTANDING ACHIEVEMENT IN THE FIELD OF

- ☐ OVERALL AWESOMENESS
- ☐ SARTORIAL SPLENDIFEROUSNESS
- ☐ RANDOM ACTS OF COOLNESS
- ☐ GENERAL OVER-AND-ABOVENESS
- ☐ EXTREME ADORABLENESS
- ☐ EXCEPTIONAL SMARTNESS
- ☐ PERSONALITY PLUSNESS
- ☐ SUPREME KINDNESS
- ☐ _____

BESTOWED THIS DAY ____ / ____ / ____ BY _____

"WINNER, WINNER, CHICKEN DINNER"

BEST EVER

WHEREAS IT HAS BEEN DETERMINED THAT YOUR EFFORTS AND ACCOMPLISHMENTS HAVE NOT GONE UNNOTICED, THIS CERTIFICATE OF APPRECIATION HEREBY PROCLAIMS THAT:

YOU WIN
THE BEST

_____

EVER

AWARD

PRESENTED TO

_____

FOR OUTSTANDING ACHIEVEMENT IN THE FIELD OF

- ☐ OVERALL AWESOMENESS
- ☐ SARTORIAL SPLENDIFEROUSNESS
- ☐ RANDOM ACTS OF COOLNESS
- ☐ GENERAL OVER-AND-ABOVENESS
- ☐ EXTREME ADORABLENESS
- ☐ EXCEPTIONAL SMARTNESS
- ☐ PERSONALITY PLUSNESS
- ☐ SUPREME KINDNESS
- ☐ _____

BESTOWED THIS DAY _____ / _____ / _____ BY _____

"WINNER, WINNER, CHICKEN DINNER"

BEST EVER

WHEREAS IT HAS BEEN DETERMINED THAT YOUR EFFORTS AND ACCOMPLISHMENTS HAVE NOT GONE UNNOTICED, THIS CERTIFICATE OF APPRECIATION HEREBY PROCLAIMS THAT:

YOU WIN

THE BEST

_____

EVER

AWARD

PRESENTED TO

_____

FOR OUTSTANDING ACHIEVEMENT IN THE FIELD OF

- ☐ OVERALL AWESOMENESS
- ☐ SARTORIAL SPLENDIFEROUSNESS
- ☐ RANDOM ACTS OF COOLNESS
- ☐ GENERAL OVER-AND-ABOVENESS
- ☐ EXTREME ADORABLENESS
- ☐ EXCEPTIONAL SMARTNESS
- ☐ PERSONALITY PLUSNESS
- ☐ SUPREME KINDNESS
- ☐ _____

BESTOWED THIS DAY ____ / ____ / ____ BY _____

"WINNER, WINNER, CHICKEN DINNER"

BEST EVER

WHEREAS IT HAS BEEN DETERMINED THAT YOUR EFFORTS AND ACCOMPLISHMENTS
HAVE NOT GONE UNNOTICED, THIS CERTIFICATE OF APPRECIATION HEREBY PROCLAIMS THAT:

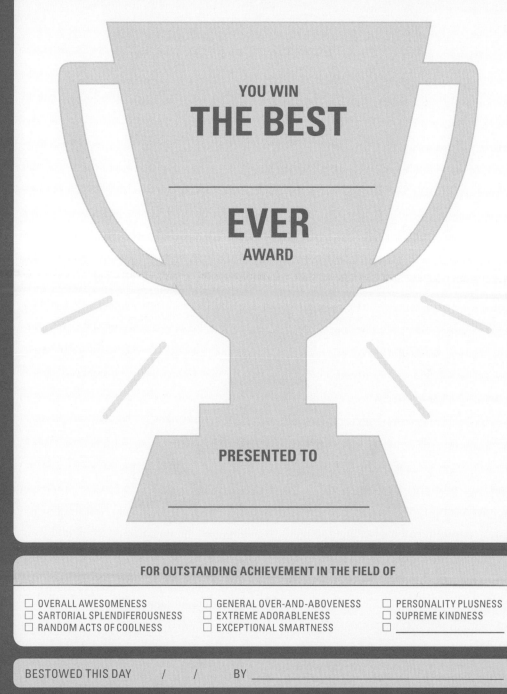

YOU WIN
THE BEST

_____

EVER

AWARD

PRESENTED TO

_____

FOR OUTSTANDING ACHIEVEMENT IN THE FIELD OF

☐ OVERALL AWESOMENESS   ☐ GENERAL OVER-AND-ABOVENESS   ☐ PERSONALITY PLUSNESS
☐ SARTORIAL SPLENDIFEROUSNESS   ☐ EXTREME ADORABLENESS   ☐ SUPREME KINDNESS
☐ RANDOM ACTS OF COOLNESS   ☐ EXCEPTIONAL SMARTNESS   ☐ _____

BESTOWED THIS DAY   /   /   BY _____

"WINNER, WINNER, CHICKEN DINNER"

BEST EVER

YOU WIN

THE BEST

_____

EVER

AWARD

PRESENTED TO

_____

FOR OUTSTANDING ACHIEVEMENT IN THE FIELD OF

☐ OVERALL AWESOMENESS
☐ SARTORIAL SPLENDIFEROUSNESS
☐ RANDOM ACTS OF COOLNESS

☐ GENERAL OVER-AND-ABOVENESS
☐ EXTREME ADORABLENESS
☐ EXCEPTIONAL SMARTNESS

☐ PERSONALITY PLUSNESS
☐ SUPREME KINDNESS
☐ _____

BESTOWED THIS DAY _____ / _____ / _____ BY _____

"WINNER, WINNER, CHICKEN DINNER"

BEST EVER

WHEREAS IT HAS BEEN DETERMINED THAT YOUR EFFORTS AND ACCOMPLISHMENTS HAVE NOT GONE UNNOTICED, THIS CERTIFICATE OF APPRECIATION HEREBY PROCLAIMS THAT:

YOU WIN
THE BEST

_____

EVER
AWARD

PRESENTED TO

_____

FOR OUTSTANDING ACHIEVEMENT IN THE FIELD OF

☐ OVERALL AWESOMENESS
☐ SARTORIAL SPLENDIFEROUSNESS
☐ RANDOM ACTS OF COOLNESS

☐ GENERAL OVER-AND-ABOVENESS
☐ EXTREME ADORABLENESS
☐ EXCEPTIONAL SMARTNESS

☐ PERSONALITY PLUSNESS
☐ SUPREME KINDNESS
☐ _____

BESTOWED THIS DAY ___ / ___ / ___ BY _____

"WINNER, WINNER, CHICKEN DINNER"

BEST EVER

WHEREAS IT HAS BEEN DETERMINED THAT YOUR EFFORTS AND ACCOMPLISHMENTS
HAVE NOT GONE UNNOTICED, THIS CERTIFICATE OF APPRECIATION HEREBY PROCLAIMS THAT:

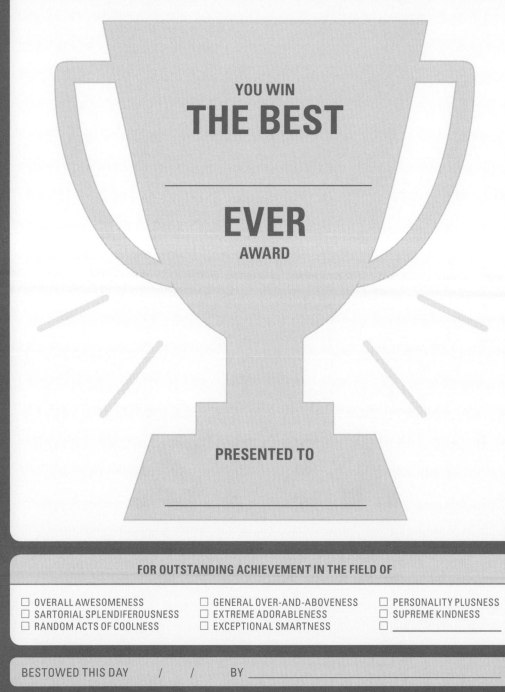

YOU WIN
THE BEST

_____

EVER

AWARD

PRESENTED TO

_____

FOR OUTSTANDING ACHIEVEMENT IN THE FIELD OF

- ☐ OVERALL AWESOMENESS
- ☐ SARTORIAL SPLENDIFEROUSNESS
- ☐ RANDOM ACTS OF COOLNESS
- ☐ GENERAL OVER-AND-ABOVENESS
- ☐ EXTREME ADORABLENESS
- ☐ EXCEPTIONAL SMARTNESS
- ☐ PERSONALITY PLUSNESS
- ☐ SUPREME KINDNESS
- ☐ _____

BESTOWED THIS DAY ____ / ____ / ____ BY _____

"WINNER, WINNER, CHICKEN DINNER"

BEST EVER

YOU WIN

THE BEST

_____

EVER

AWARD

PRESENTED TO

_____

FOR OUTSTANDING ACHIEVEMENT IN THE FIELD OF

☐ OVERALL AWESOMENESS   ☐ GENERAL OVER-AND-ABOVENESS   ☐ PERSONALITY PLUSNESS
☐ SARTORIAL SPLENDIFEROUSNESS   ☐ EXTREME ADORABLENESS   ☐ SUPREME KINDNESS
☐ RANDOM ACTS OF COOLNESS   ☐ EXCEPTIONAL SMARTNESS   ☐ _____

BESTOWED THIS DAY   /   /   BY _____

"WINNER, WINNER, CHICKEN DINNER"

BEST EVER

YOU WIN

THE BEST

_____

EVER

AWARD

PRESENTED TO

_____

FOR OUTSTANDING ACHIEVEMENT IN THE FIELD OF

- ☐ OVERALL AWESOMENESS
- ☐ SARTORIAL SPLENDIFEROUSNESS
- ☐ RANDOM ACTS OF COOLNESS
- ☐ GENERAL OVER-AND-ABOVENESS
- ☐ EXTREME ADORABLENESS
- ☐ EXCEPTIONAL SMARTNESS
- ☐ PERSONALITY PLUSNESS
- ☐ SUPREME KINDNESS
- ☐ _____

BESTOWED THIS DAY ___ / ___ / ___ BY _____

"WINNER, WINNER, CHICKEN DINNER"

BEST EVER

WHEREAS IT HAS BEEN DETERMINED THAT YOUR EFFORTS AND ACCOMPLISHMENTS HAVE NOT GONE UNNOTICED, THIS CERTIFICATE OF APPRECIATION HEREBY PROCLAIMS THAT:

YOU WIN
THE BEST

_____

EVER
AWARD

PRESENTED TO

_____

FOR OUTSTANDING ACHIEVEMENT IN THE FIELD OF

☐ OVERALL AWESOMENESS
☐ SARTORIAL SPLENDIFEROUSNESS
☐ RANDOM ACTS OF COOLNESS

☐ GENERAL OVER-AND-ABOVENESS
☐ EXTREME ADORABLENESS
☐ EXCEPTIONAL SMARTNESS

☐ PERSONALITY PLUSNESS
☐ SUPREME KINDNESS
☐ _____

BESTOWED THIS DAY   /   /   BY _____

"WINNER, WINNER, CHICKEN DINNER"

BEST EVER

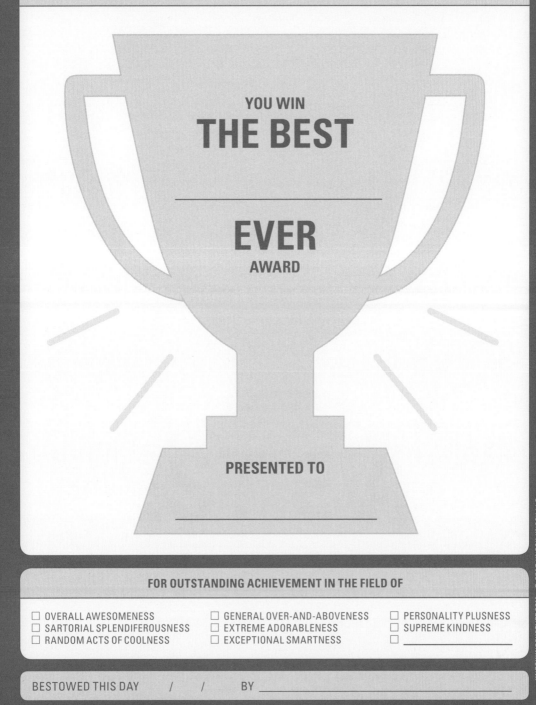

WHEREAS IT HAS BEEN DETERMINED THAT YOUR EFFORTS AND ACCOMPLISHMENTS HAVE NOT GONE UNNOTICED, THIS CERTIFICATE OF APPRECIATION HEREBY PROCLAIMS THAT:

YOU WIN

THE BEST

_____

EVER

AWARD

PRESENTED TO

_____

FOR OUTSTANDING ACHIEVEMENT IN THE FIELD OF

☐ OVERALL AWESOMENESS
☐ SARTORIAL SPLENDIFEROUSNESS
☐ RANDOM ACTS OF COOLNESS

☐ GENERAL OVER-AND-ABOVENESS
☐ EXTREME ADORABLENESS
☐ EXCEPTIONAL SMARTNESS

☐ PERSONALITY PLUSNESS
☐ SUPREME KINDNESS
☐ _____

BESTOWED THIS DAY   /   /   BY _____

"WINNER, WINNER, CHICKEN DINNER"

BEST EVER

WHEREAS IT HAS BEEN DETERMINED THAT YOUR EFFORTS AND ACCOMPLISHMENTS HAVE NOT GONE UNNOTICED, THIS CERTIFICATE OF APPRECIATION HEREBY PROCLAIMS THAT:

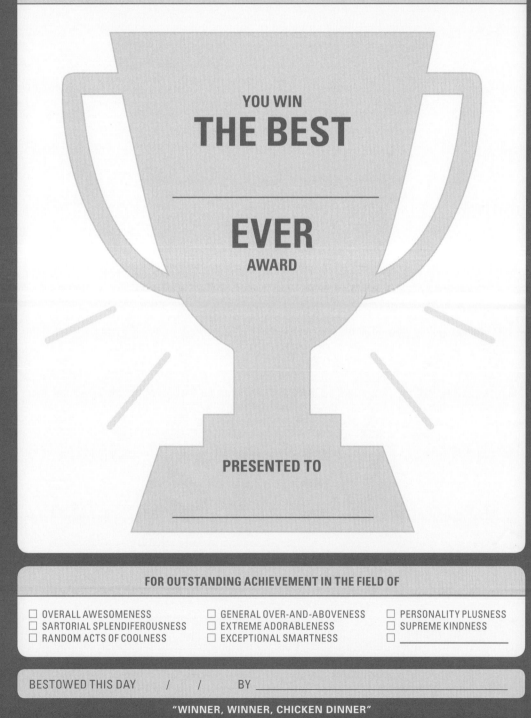

YOU WIN
THE BEST

_____

EVER
AWARD

PRESENTED TO

_____

FOR OUTSTANDING ACHIEVEMENT IN THE FIELD OF

☐ OVERALL AWESOMENESS
☐ SARTORIAL SPLENDIFEROUSNESS
☐ RANDOM ACTS OF COOLNESS

☐ GENERAL OVER-AND-ABOVENESS
☐ EXTREME ADORABLENESS
☐ EXCEPTIONAL SMARTNESS

☐ PERSONALITY PLUSNESS
☐ SUPREME KINDNESS
☐ _____

BESTOWED THIS DAY ___ / ___ / ___ BY _____

"WINNER, WINNER, CHICKEN DINNER"

BEST EVER

WHEREAS IT HAS BEEN DETERMINED THAT YOUR EFFORTS AND ACCOMPLISHMENTS HAVE NOT GONE UNNOTICED, THIS CERTIFICATE OF APPRECIATION HEREBY PROCLAIMS THAT:

YOU WIN

THE BEST

_____

EVER

AWARD

PRESENTED TO

_____

FOR OUTSTANDING ACHIEVEMENT IN THE FIELD OF

☐ OVERALL AWESOMENESS
☐ SARTORIAL SPLENDIFEROUSNESS
☐ RANDOM ACTS OF COOLNESS

☐ GENERAL OVER-AND-ABOVENESS
☐ EXTREME ADORABLENESS
☐ EXCEPTIONAL SMARTNESS

☐ PERSONALITY PLUSNESS
☐ SUPREME KINDNESS
☐ _____

BESTOWED THIS DAY ___ / ___ / ___ BY _____

"WINNER, WINNER, CHICKEN DINNER"

BEST EVER

WHEREAS IT HAS BEEN DETERMINED THAT YOUR EFFORTS AND ACCOMPLISHMENTS HAVE NOT GONE UNNOTICED, THIS CERTIFICATE OF APPRECIATION HEREBY PROCLAIMS THAT:

YOU WIN

THE BEST

_____

EVER

AWARD

PRESENTED TO

_____

FOR OUTSTANDING ACHIEVEMENT IN THE FIELD OF

- ☐ OVERALL AWESOMENESS
- ☐ SARTORIAL SPLENDIFEROUSNESS
- ☐ RANDOM ACTS OF COOLNESS
- ☐ GENERAL OVER-AND-ABOVENESS
- ☐ EXTREME ADORABLENESS
- ☐ EXCEPTIONAL SMARTNESS
- ☐ PERSONALITY PLUSNESS
- ☐ SUPREME KINDNESS
- ☐ _____

BESTOWED THIS DAY   /   /   BY _____

"WINNER, WINNER, CHICKEN DINNER"

BEST EVER

WHEREAS IT HAS BEEN DETERMINED THAT YOUR EFFORTS AND ACCOMPLISHMENTS HAVE NOT GONE UNNOTICED, THIS CERTIFICATE OF APPRECIATION HEREBY PROCLAIMS THAT:

YOU WIN
THE BEST

_____

EVER
AWARD

PRESENTED TO

_____

FOR OUTSTANDING ACHIEVEMENT IN THE FIELD OF

- ☐ OVERALL AWESOMENESS
- ☐ SARTORIAL SPLENDIFEROUSNESS
- ☐ RANDOM ACTS OF COOLNESS
- ☐ GENERAL OVER-AND-ABOVENESS
- ☐ EXTREME ADORABLENESS
- ☐ EXCEPTIONAL SMARTNESS
- ☐ PERSONALITY PLUSNESS
- ☐ SUPREME KINDNESS
- ☐ _____

BESTOWED THIS DAY   /   /   BY _____

"WINNER, WINNER, CHICKEN DINNER"

BEST EVER

BEST EVER

WHEREAS IT HAS BEEN DETERMINED THAT YOUR EFFORTS AND ACCOMPLISHMENTS HAVE NOT GONE UNNOTICED, THIS CERTIFICATE OF APPRECIATION HEREBY PROCLAIMS THAT:

YOU WIN

THE BEST

_____

EVER

AWARD

PRESENTED TO

_____

FOR OUTSTANDING ACHIEVEMENT IN THE FIELD OF

- ☐ OVERALL AWESOMENESS
- ☐ SARTORIAL SPLENDIFEROUSNESS
- ☐ RANDOM ACTS OF COOLNESS
- ☐ GENERAL OVER-AND-ABOVENESS
- ☐ EXTREME ADORABLENESS
- ☐ EXCEPTIONAL SMARTNESS
- ☐ PERSONALITY PLUSNESS
- ☐ SUPREME KINDNESS
- ☐ _____

BESTOWED THIS DAY ____ / ____ / ____ BY _____

"WINNER, WINNER, CHICKEN DINNER"

BEST EVER

YOU WIN

THE BEST

_____

EVER

AWARD

PRESENTED TO

_____

FOR OUTSTANDING ACHIEVEMENT IN THE FIELD OF

- ☐ OVERALL AWESOMENESS
- ☐ SARTORIAL SPLENDIFEROUSNESS
- ☐ RANDOM ACTS OF COOLNESS
- ☐ GENERAL OVER-AND-ABOVENESS
- ☐ EXTREME ADORABLENESS
- ☐ EXCEPTIONAL SMARTNESS
- ☐ PERSONALITY PLUSNESS
- ☐ SUPREME KINDNESS
- ☐ _____

BESTOWED THIS DAY ___ / ___ / ___ BY _____

"WINNER, WINNER, CHICKEN DINNER"

BEST EVER

YOU WIN

THE BEST

_____

EVER

AWARD

PRESENTED TO

_____

FOR OUTSTANDING ACHIEVEMENT IN THE FIELD OF

- ☐ OVERALL AWESOMENESS
- ☐ SARTORIAL SPLENDIFEROUSNESS
- ☐ RANDOM ACTS OF COOLNESS
- ☐ GENERAL OVER-AND-ABOVENESS
- ☐ EXTREME ADORABLENESS
- ☐ EXCEPTIONAL SMARTNESS
- ☐ PERSONALITY PLUSNESS
- ☐ SUPREME KINDNESS
- ☐ _____

BESTOWED THIS DAY   /   /   BY _____

"WINNER, WINNER, CHICKEN DINNER"

BEST EVER

WHEREAS IT HAS BEEN DETERMINED THAT YOUR EFFORTS AND ACCOMPLISHMENTS HAVE NOT GONE UNNOTICED, THIS CERTIFICATE OF APPRECIATION HEREBY PROCLAIMS THAT:

YOU WIN
THE BEST
_____
EVER
AWARD

PRESENTED TO

_____

FOR OUTSTANDING ACHIEVEMENT IN THE FIELD OF

☐ OVERALL AWESOMENESS
☐ SARTORIAL SPLENDIFEROUSNESS
☐ RANDOM ACTS OF COOLNESS

☐ GENERAL OVER-AND-ABOVENESS
☐ EXTREME ADORABLENESS
☐ EXCEPTIONAL SMARTNESS

☐ PERSONALITY PLUSNESS
☐ SUPREME KINDNESS
☐ _____

BESTOWED THIS DAY   /   /   BY _____

"WINNER, WINNER, CHICKEN DINNER"

BEST EVER

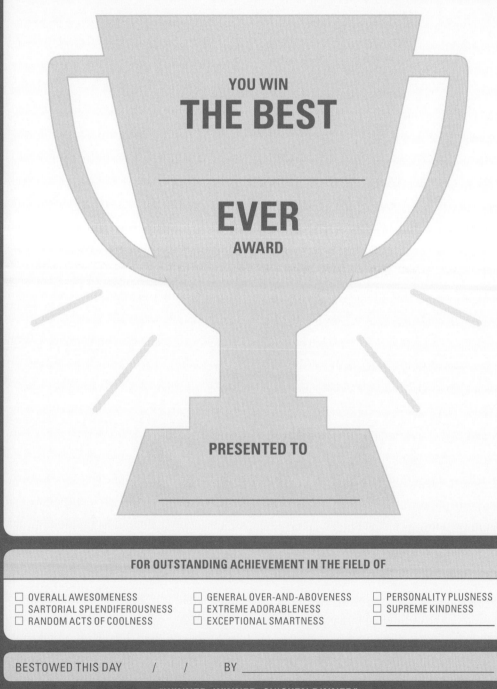

WHEREAS IT HAS BEEN DETERMINED THAT YOUR EFFORTS AND ACCOMPLISHMENTS HAVE NOT GONE UNNOTICED, THIS CERTIFICATE OF APPRECIATION HEREBY PROCLAIMS THAT:

YOU WIN

THE BEST

_____

EVER

AWARD

PRESENTED TO

_____

FOR OUTSTANDING ACHIEVEMENT IN THE FIELD OF

- ☐ OVERALL AWESOMENESS
- ☐ SARTORIAL SPLENDIFEROUSNESS
- ☐ RANDOM ACTS OF COOLNESS
- ☐ GENERAL OVER-AND-ABOVENESS
- ☐ EXTREME ADORABLENESS
- ☐ EXCEPTIONAL SMARTNESS
- ☐ PERSONALITY PLUSNESS
- ☐ SUPREME KINDNESS
- ☐ _____

BESTOWED THIS DAY   /   /   BY _____

"WINNER, WINNER, CHICKEN DINNER"

BEST EVER

YOU WIN

THE BEST

_____

EVER

AWARD

PRESENTED TO

_____

FOR OUTSTANDING ACHIEVEMENT IN THE FIELD OF

- ☐ OVERALL AWESOMENESS
- ☐ SARTORIAL SPLENDIFEROUSNESS
- ☐ RANDOM ACTS OF COOLNESS
- ☐ GENERAL OVER-AND-ABOVENESS
- ☐ EXTREME ADORABLENESS
- ☐ EXCEPTIONAL SMARTNESS
- ☐ PERSONALITY PLUSNESS
- ☐ SUPREME KINDNESS
- ☐ _____

BESTOWED THIS DAY   /   /   BY _____

"WINNER, WINNER, CHICKEN DINNER"

BEST EVER

WHEREAS IT HAS BEEN DETERMINED THAT YOUR EFFORTS AND ACCOMPLISHMENTS HAVE NOT GONE UNNOTICED, THIS CERTIFICATE OF APPRECIATION HEREBY PROCLAIMS THAT:

YOU WIN
THE BEST

_____

EVER
AWARD

PRESENTED TO

_____

FOR OUTSTANDING ACHIEVEMENT IN THE FIELD OF

☐ OVERALL AWESOMENESS
☐ SARTORIAL SPLENDIFEROUSNESS
☐ RANDOM ACTS OF COOLNESS

☐ GENERAL OVER-AND-ABOVENESS
☐ EXTREME ADORABLENESS
☐ EXCEPTIONAL SMARTNESS

☐ PERSONALITY PLUSNESS
☐ SUPREME KINDNESS
☐ _____

BESTOWED THIS DAY _____ / _____ / _____ BY _____

"WINNER, WINNER, CHICKEN DINNER"

BEST EVER

WHEREAS IT HAS BEEN DETERMINED THAT YOUR EFFORTS AND ACCOMPLISHMENTS HAVE NOT GONE UNNOTICED, THIS CERTIFICATE OF APPRECIATION HEREBY PROCLAIMS THAT:

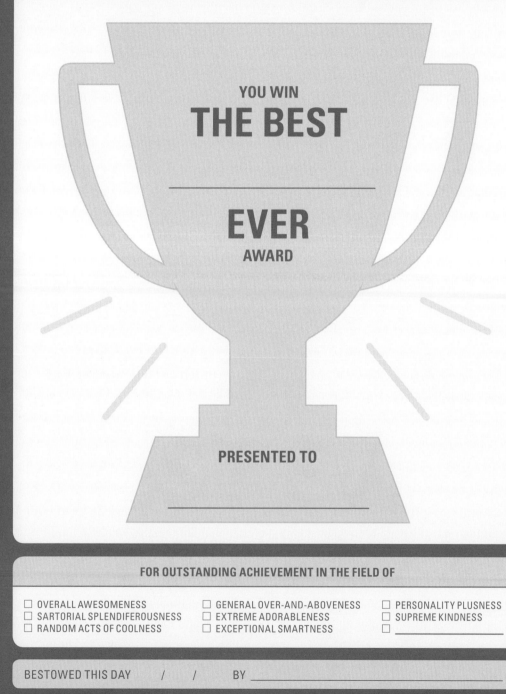

YOU WIN
THE BEST

_____

EVER
AWARD

PRESENTED TO

_____

FOR OUTSTANDING ACHIEVEMENT IN THE FIELD OF

☐ OVERALL AWESOMENESS
☐ SARTORIAL SPLENDIFEROUSNESS
☐ RANDOM ACTS OF COOLNESS

☐ GENERAL OVER-AND-ABOVENESS
☐ EXTREME ADORABLENESS
☐ EXCEPTIONAL SMARTNESS

☐ PERSONALITY PLUSNESS
☐ SUPREME KINDNESS
☐ _____

BESTOWED THIS DAY ___ / ___ / ___ BY _____

"WINNER, WINNER, CHICKEN DINNER"